A DIFFERENT HOME

Tana Reiff

A Different Home

Tana Reiff
AR B.L.: 2.9
Points: 1.0   UG

HOPES *And* DREAMS

Hungry No More
For Gold and Blood
O Little Town
Push to the West
Nobody Knows
Old Ways, New Ways
Little Italy
A Different Home
Boat People
The Magic Paper

Cover Photo: AP/Wide World Photos
Illustration: Tennessee Dixon

ISBN 0-8224-3684-1
Printed in the United States of America

7 8 9 10 11   08 07 06 05 04

Globe
Fearon

Pearson Learning Group

1-800-321-3106
www.pearsonlearning.com

CONTENTS

CHAPTER 1
Over Cuba, 1960

"Look hard,"
said Mario Lopez
to the little boy.
"You can still see
the sugar cane fields."
He pointed
out the airplane window.

Mario had to speak up.
The plane's engines
were very loud.
He pulled the boy
close to the window.
The little boy
pressed his face
against the glass.

"See down there!"
shouted Mario.
"The sugar cane season
is almost over now."

"I can tell,"
said the boy.
"The fields
look more brown than green."

"Ah, it is hard
to say goodbye
to our home!"
said Mario.
"The Cubans
grow such sweet cane.
The people
make such fine sugar.
My family
owned a sugar business.
I helped them.
We sent sugar
all over the world."

"Then why
are you flying

to the United States?"
asked the boy.

"Try to understand,"
said Mario.
"Cuba has seen
a big change.
Some new leaders
took over the country.
Now some people
no longer fit in.
And some other people
must start all over.
My parents stayed in Cuba
to run the business.
Only now,
the country owns it.
They sent me
to work in the United States.
They feel
I will be better off
in the United States.
Maybe they will come later."

"My parents
are sending me

to live with my aunt and uncle,"
said the little boy.

"You will be OK,"
Mario told him.
But he worried
about his own parents.
Mama and Papa
were left with very little.
Would they be all right?

He looked down
at his clothes.
He carried
another shirt in his bag.
That was all he had.
In Cuba,
he owned
lots of clothes.
He had everything
he ever needed.
He knew
life would be different now.

Mario looked
out the window again.

With each passing second,
the island of Cuba
grew smaller.
Before long,
Cuba was a tiny dot
in the ocean.
In another minute,
it was out of sight.
In all his 23 years,
Mario had never felt
so sad.

"When can we
go back home to Cuba?"
asked the little boy.

"Soon, I hope,"
said Mario.
"The trouble will die down.
We will go home.
You wait and see."

It was only a short trip
to Miami, Florida.
An hour later
the plane touched ground.

Thinking It Over

1. Have you ever been
   on an airplane?
   How did you feel
   when you saw the ground below?

2. Why do Mario's parents
   want him to live
   in the United States?

3. Do you think
   the people on the airplane
   will ever go back to Cuba?

CHAPTER 2

Many, many other Cubans
came to Miami, too.
The city
was old and run-down.
But the weather
was warm,
like in Cuba.
That was just fine
with the Cubans.
Most of them
wanted to stay
right here.
Besides,
there were so many others
to speak Spanish with.

Mario got off the plane.
The first order of business
was to check in.
Like everyone else,
Mario answered questions.

The little boy
from the plane
found his aunt and uncle.
Mario said goodbye
to him.

Then Mario was sent
to a house for Cubans.
He could stay there
until he found
a place to live.
There he met
a new friend.
The young man's name
was Domingo Ruiz.

"We could go
to the Cuban Refugee Center,"
said Domingo.
"They can help us
find a job.
They will give us money
to buy food."

"I do not want
free handouts,"

said Mario.
"I will find my own job.
I will make
my own money.
And soon enough,
I will go home
to Cuba."

   Mario did find
a job.
He went to work
in a food store.
He and Domingo
moved into two rooms
in an old house.
Three nights a week
Mario went to school.
He already knew
some English.
But he wanted
to learn more.
Some nights
he felt too tired
to go to school.
Even so,
he never missed a class.

Mario was not happy
with his job.
He had helped his parents
run a big business.
Now he cut open cartons.
He took out
boxes and jars.
He stamped prices
on each thing.
He placed the food
on the shelves.
He was not used
to this kind of work.

Back home,
Mario wore
a white shirt and long silk tie
to work.
Now he had to wear
a white apron.
He felt out of place.

Back home,
Mario had worked
with a lot of money.
The food store

would not let him
handle any money.

"I need
a different job!"
said Mario one night.
"I don't mind
hard work.
I don't mind
long hours.
But I am not cut out
for the food store."

"Then why don't you go
to the Cuban Refugee Center?"
said Domingo.
"The people there
want to help Cubans.
Maybe they
can help you
find the right job."

"All right,"
said Mario.
"I'll go there
tomorrow morning."

Thinking It Over

1. How would you feel
   if you had a job
   that was not right for you?

2. Is it hard for you
   to ask for help?

CHAPTER 3

Mario went
to the Cuban Refugee Center
the next day.
It was a white building
with two stories.
There were Cubans
all over the place.
Mario knew some of them
from back home.

"What are you good at?"
a woman there asked.

"Back home
I helped to run
a big sugar business,"
said Mario in English.
"I know lots
about business.
I am good
with numbers.

I come up
with bright ideas."

"And you speak English
very well,"
said the woman.
"Have you ever worked
in a bank?"

"No,"
said Mario.
"But I have worked
with a bank.
I know how banks work!"

"There's a job
for you
in Ohio,"
said the woman.
"It's in a bank.
They need someone
who can speak
Spanish and English.
You will help the bank
do business
with Spanish-speaking people.

We will pay your way
to Ohio.
We will also give you
50 dollars.
It will help you
get on your feet.
A church in Ohio
will set you up
with a place to live."

"Ohio?"
Mario asked.
"That's up north!
I do not want
to leave Miami.
When it's time
to return to Cuba
I want to be here!"

"Don't worry,"
said the woman.
"We will pay your way back
if the time comes."

"And what if my parents
decide to leave Cuba?"

asked Mario.
"How will they find me?"

"We can get word
to you,"
said the woman.
"But I must tell you this.
Cubans are waiting
to get out.
There are not
enough airplanes
for everyone.
Leaving Cuba
is getting very hard."

This was all bad news
for Mario.
He put his head down.
"I have never lived
in cold weather,"
he said.
"And I may be
the only Cuban in Ohio.
I don't know
if I should go
to Ohio."

"There are not
enough jobs
here in Miami,"
said the woman.

"All right,"
said Mario.

He went
to tell Domingo
he was leaving Miami.
Mario was not happy
to be going away.
He wished
his whole family
had left Cuba together.

A week later,
Mario left
for Ohio.
One year ago
he had left Cuba,
his first home.
Now he was leaving
the other Cubans
in Miami.

He took a train
to Ohio.
He sat by a window.
He watched the corn fields
rush by.
It was as if
his past
were rushing by
as fast as the train.
Where was home?
Where had it gone?
Would he ever find it?

A man in blue
walked up
to Mario's seat.
"Would you care
for a pillow?"
he asked.

"Yes, thank you,"
said Mario
in English.
But in his sleep
he still dreamed
in Spanish.

Thinking It Over

1. What are you good at?
   How would you go about
   finding a job you like?

2. Would you take the job
   in Ohio?

3. Do you worry much?
   What do you worry about?

CHAPTER **4**

The church in Ohio
had a home
all ready for Mario.
There was food
in the kitchen.
There were chairs and beds.
There was even
a TV set.
A freshly baked cake
sat on the kitchen table.
The cake said "Welcome"
in big green letters.

The place
had only three rooms.
In Cuba,
Mario had lived
in a fine, big house.
But the warm welcome
made Mario feel
not so far from home.

Still, he knew
his life as a child
was far behind him now.

The Ohio winter
was very cold.
Some snowy mornings
Mario had to wait
a very long time
for the bus.
His face got so cold
that it burned.
His hands
felt like ice.
Mario loved his new job
at the bank.
But on days like this
he wished he could fly
back to Cuba.

At the same time
the news from Cuba
was bad.
He read the paper.
And now and then
he got a letter

from his parents.
Things in Cuba
were only getting worse.
He didn't talk about it
with anyone.
He didn't think
the people at the bank
would understand
how he felt.

Then Mario
heard some good news.
The United States
was flying people
out of Cuba.
He wrote a letter
to Mama and Papa.
"Leave Cuba now!"
he begged them.
He waited
to hear their answer.
But no word came.

Another Cuban
came to work

at the bank.
His name
was Luis Otero.
At last,
Mario had someone
to talk to.

One day
Mario spoke up
about Cuba.
"My parents
are still there,"
he said.
"I worry
about them.
Now I hear
the United States
has a list of names.
They will try
to get these people
out of Cuba.
I could put my parents
on the list.
Maybe this
would speed things up."

"Maybe the list
could help your parents,"
said Luis.
"But it could also
get them into trouble.
I think
you should wait."

"You are probably right,"
said Mario.
"Besides,
we may still be able
to go home ourselves."

"You know
things don't look good,"
said Luis.
"We might be here
a long time.
We must get on
with life."

"I try
not to get my hopes up,"
said Mario.

"But I do wonder
what tomorrow holds."

That night
Mario wrote a letter
to the Cuban Refugee Center.
He sent along
a check for 50 dollars.
"Thank you for your help,"
he wrote.
"This country
has been good to me.
I know
the 50 dollars
was a gift.
But I want
to pay it back.
At last I can.
Now I am
on my own."

Thinking It Over

1. Does everyone need someone to talk to?

2. Would you have paid back the gift of 50 dollars?

3. Do you get on with your life, or hold back for some reason?

CHAPTER 5

During the next two years
Mario did well.
He got a raise
at the bank.
He began to work
with Spanish-speaking countries.

But Mama and Papa
were still in Cuba.
And time
was passing.

One night
Mario and Luis
went out to dinner.
Luis brought up Cuba.
"Our chance
of going home
is growing small,"
he said.
"In fact,

sometimes I wonder.
Are we Cubans
or Americans?
We seem to be
something in between.
So I have been thinking.
Perhaps the time has come
to become real Americans."

Mario looked up.
His face
turned to stone.

"I didn't mean
to frighten you!"
Luis laughed.
"But let's face facts.
We may be here
as long as we live.
We should be able
to vote.
As it is,
we can't even
take business trips
outside the U.S.
We should be able

to do everything
an American can do."

    "You are right,"
said Mario
in a soft voice.
"I never wanted
to think about this.
But we must.
However,
we don't even have
green cards.
To become a citizen,
you must first have
a green card."

    "Haven't you heard?
Now we Cubans
can get green cards,"
said Luis.
"Let's become citizens!
Let's do this together!
I vote yes!"

    "In the United States,
the people vote

on everything!"
laughed Mario.
"All right.
I vote yes, too!"

    "Then that is that,"
said Luis.
"The green card
is the first step.
Second,
we must live
in the United States
for five years.
It's only three years
if you are married
to an American."

    "Maybe we can marry
American women!"
laughed Mario.
"Oh, well—
we have lived here
almost five years.
What else do we need?"

"We must fill out
a form,"
said Luis.
"We must each send along
three pictures.
And we must send along
our fingerprints.
Then someone
sits down
and asks us questions."

"What questions?"
Mario asked.

"Oh, questions
about the United States.
Like how it runs.
They don't ask everyone
the same questions.
They might ask you
how many people
each state sends
to Washington.
They might ask me
about the Bill of Rights."

"Must we pass
an English test?"
Mario asked.

"No,"
said Luis.
"But we must know
enough English
to answer the questions."

"I can do that,"
said Mario.

"And here is
the best part,"
said Luis.
"After all this,
you stand up
in court.
You say you will be
a good American.
You pledge
to the flag
of the United States.
And then they tell you
you are an American!"

"I don't know
if I can do that,"
said Mario.
"I am a Cuban.
I grew up there.
It will be hard
to let go
of the past."

"I try to remember
my Mama's words,"
said Luis.
"Home is where
the heart is.
My heart and I
are in Ohio!
Don't you see?"

Thinking It Over

1. Do you believe "home is where the heart is"?

2. Do you think it is too easy or too hard to become an American?

CHAPTER 6

Mario and Luis
went to a class.
They studied
to become Americans.
They sent in
their forms.
They took
their tests.
Then the big day came.

Mario and Luis
stood up in court.
They were part
of a large group.
A lot of people
became Americans
that day.

Mario fixed his eyes
on the American flag.
"I pledge allegiance

to the flag . . ."
he began.
What does this mean?
he asked himself.
I can be
a good citizen.
I can live here
for the rest
of my life.
I can follow
the laws of the land.
I can give of myself
to the United States.
But what will stay
inside me?
Will I still be Cuban
in my blood?
In my heart?
". . . with liberty
and justice for all."

He looked over
at Luis.
His friend
had a big smile
on his face.

"That is it!"
said Luis.
"We are Americans!
Let me
shake your hand,
my American friend!"

A woman
handed each of them
a tiny American flag.
"This is to remember
this special day,"
she said.

Yes,
Mario said to himself.
This is a special day.
It is the day between
yesterday and tomorrow.

Thinking It Over

1. What does it mean
   to be a citizen
   of a country?

2. Can a person
   ever forget
   his or her first home?

CHAPTER **7**

Mario met Kathy
when she came to work
at the bank.
He liked her
right away.

Kathy was not so sure
about Mario.
She was a small-town girl
from Ohio.
In her town
no one was Cuban.
To Kathy,
Mario was different.

Even so,
she saw Mario often.
She could not help
but like him.
She wanted him
to meet her family.

"What if
they don't like me?"
he asked her.

"How can they not?"
laughed Kathy.
"You are nice.
You are smart.
You are an American.
What more
can they want for me?"

"You forgot to say
I speak good English!"
Mario added.
"But many people
still think of me
as strange.
My voice
still has a touch of Spanish.
And remember,
I still have a Spanish name."

"There is nothing wrong
with you,"
said Kathy.

So Mario and Kathy
drove to Kathy's home.
It was winter.
Ohio looked beautiful
under its first snow
of the year.

"I'd like you
to meet Mario Lopez,"
said Kathy
to her parents.

"How nice
to meet you,"
said Kathy's mother.
She stared at Mario.
"Our Kathy
has never brought home
a Spanish young man."

Mario felt strange
when she said that.
Why did the woman
have to think of him
as Spanish?
Why did she

think of him
as anything at all?

As the night went on,
things got better.
Kathy's parents
enjoyed Mario's stories.
He told them
about coming
from Cuba.
He told them
about starting all over.
He told them
how his parents
were still in Cuba.
Kathy's parents
came to understand
Mario Lopez
a little better.

Soon it was time
to go home.
"We hope
to see your friend again,"
said Kathy's mother.

"You can count on that,"
said Kathy.
She smiled
at Mario.
He smiled back.
At that second,
he knew
that she would marry him.

Thinking It Over

1. Have you ever liked
   or disliked people
   before you met them?

2. Have you ever felt different
   from everyone else?

3. Why can understanding a person
   help you like him or her?

CHAPTER 8

The next summer,
Mario and Kathy got married.
Luis Otero
was Mario's best man.

Now Mario and Kathy
needed a place to live.
They looked
in the paper.
They went to see
the places
that looked interesting.

"Mr. and Mrs. Mario Lopez . . ."
said one landlord.
"We would rather
keep the place American."

"But we *are* American,"
said Mario.

"Oh, I see,"
said the landlord.
"You came
into the country.
You married her.
Now you're American—
is that it?"

"No,"
said Mario.
"I was an American citizen
before I met Kathy.
And why would it matter
if I were not American?"

"Well, I'm sorry,"
said the landlord.
"I don't think
you'd like this place.
Good luck
to you both."

After this had happened
with several landlords,
Mario grew angry.

"I've never seen you
this angry,"
said Kathy.

"I've never felt
this angry!"
said Mario.
"I have moved
more and more away
from my Cuban roots.
I can't even see
my own parents!
I have become
as American as anyone.
I worked my way up
like everyone else.
So I don't like
these mean questions.
It's not fair!"

"What can we do?"
asked Kathy.
"A lot of people
are afraid of people
they think are strange.

You don't want
to go back to Cuba,
do you?"

   "Of course not,"
said Mario.
"I only wish
Mama and Papa
could come here.
Or maybe I
just need a way
to keep in touch
with my roots."

   At last,
Mario and Kathy
found a place.
They lived
near Cleveland.
That is where
they started their family.

Thinking It Over

1. Do you keep in touch
   with your roots?
   How?

2. What is an "American"?

CHAPTER 9

Mario and Kathy
had two little girls.
Their names
were Barbara and Brenda.
Mario became
head of South American business
at the bank.
Many people
got to know him.
He also
gave his time
to the town.

The children
started school.
Mario and Kathy
had a lot of interest
in the school.
They helped the girls
with their homework.

They joined
the parents' group.

One day
a man from the school board
came to visit.

"Mario and Kathy,"
he began.
"I plan
to give up my seat
on the school board.
I think
one of you
should run for the school board.
I think
either of you
could win the seat."

"Not me!"
laughed Kathy.
"I'm too shy.
But why not Mario?"

"Well, why not?"
said Mario.

So Mario Lopez
ran for the school board.
Kathy helped out.
Mario's face
was on signs
all over town.
He went
on a TV talk show.
He spoke
to groups.
He felt sure
he could do
a good job.
But first
he needed votes.
He needed
all kinds of people
behind him.

The day came
to vote.

"I cannot believe this!"
said Mario.
"Not only can I vote.

I can vote for myself."

    All the hard work
paid off.
Mario won
the school board seat.
That night
Mario and Kathy
threw a big party.
It lasted
long into the night.

    Brenda cried
when Mario
put her to bed.
"It is past
your bedtime.
You are very tired,"
Mario told her.

    "My friends
saw you on TV,"
she said.
"They said
you talk funny."

"That is because
I come from Cuba,"
said Mario.
"When I first spoke,
I spoke Spanish.
I had to learn English
when I was older."

He turned off the light.
He walked
down the stairs.
He looked
around the house.
It didn't look Cuban
at all.
After all these years,
he still missed
his Cuban roots.
He still wanted
to find them.
He still did not know
how to do it.

Thinking It Over

1. Do you vote?
   Why or why not?

2. Would you vote
   for someone like Mario?

3. What makes a home
   feel like home?

CHAPTER 10

"Look at this
in the paper,"
said Kathy one morning.
"People can travel
to Cuba now.
You may not do business there.
You may not spend money.
But you may visit!"

"I must go!"
cried Mario.
"Maybe Mama and Papa
cannot come to live here.
But after all these years,
maybe we can see each other!"

So in a few weeks
Mario flew to Cuba.
He had to go
with a group.
He made plans

to stay in a hotel
for two weeks.

As soon as
he arrived,
Mario went to see
his parents.
They now lived
in a different
part of town.
Mario had to take a bus.
Then he walked
a long way.
He got lost
and had to ask
for directions.
Finally he got there.
Mario's heart was pounding.
He knocked on the door.
There were voices inside.
Then the door opened.

"Mama! Papa!"
cried Mario.
He put his arms
around both of them.

He couldn't hold them
close enough!
Their heads
were gray now.
But their eyes
were full of love.

Mario looked
around their house.
Their old house
had been very large.
This house
was small and simple.
It was clear
that Mama and Papa
were no longer well off.
But they
seemed to be all right.
Maybe not as young.
Maybe not as happy.
But all right.

"Now listen to me,"
said Mario.
"I want you both
to come to the United States.

It's time
you gave up the sugar business.
Spend the rest of your years
in the United States."

   "If only we had left
when you did,"
said Mama.
"We have lost all these years
without our boy."

   "We are ready to leave,"
said Papa.
"But we can't leave
just yet.
We will let you know
if it becomes possible."

   In the next few days
Mario got to see
his home country again.
Some things about Cuba
looked the same as always.
But the country felt different.
Something about it
didn't feel like home.

Thinking It Over

1. Do you think
   it was a good idea
   for Mario to visit Cuba?

2. Is there anything
   you wish you had done
   at some time in the past?

CHAPTER 11

Three years
after Mario's trip,
Cuba began
to let people leave
for the United States.
Not just to visit,
but to live there.
Cubans in Miami
sent boats
to pick them up.

Mario waited
to hear from Mama and Papa.
He could think
of nothing else.
Weeks went by.
There was still no word.
At last,
the telephone rang.
It was Papa.

"Can you help us?"
cried Papa.
"We have waited
for three days
just to use a telephone."

"Of course,
I'll help!"
cried Mario.
"I'll rent a boat."

"We will wait
in Mariel,"
said Papa.

"I will have
a boat in Mariel
as soon as possible,"
said Mario.

The next day,
Mario went
to the head
of the bank.
"I would like the bank
to join me,"

he said.
"I need money
to rent a boat.
I want to bring my parents
and other Cubans
to the United States.
I will add
my own money.
In some way,
I will find
all the money we need."

That day
was just the start.
Mario put his whole heart
into the plan.
He wrote to Cuban groups
in Miami and New Jersey.
He asked
for their ideas.
He got money
from the bank.
He got money
from other companies.
Luis Otero
helped find money, too.

Just one week later
Mario came home
with a smile
from ear to ear.

"Kathy, this is it!"
he shouted.
"We have enough money
to rent a big boat!"

"This is great!"
said Kathy.
"What is next?"

"Now I must go
to Miami,"
said Mario.
"I must rent a boat."

Thinking It Over

1. Have you ever had
   a strong drive
   to do something important?

2. What is your favorite cause?

3. Do you think
   Mario's plan will work?

CHAPTER 12

Mario bought
a plane ticket.
He flew
to Miami
by himself.
What he found
surprised him.

It had been
20 years
since Mario was here.
Like Cuba,
Miami had changed.
Mario remembered Miami
as a run-down city.
Now it felt
a lot like the old Cuba.
Cuban people
were all over.
He heard Cuban music
blowing across the warm air.

He walked down streets
of clean, white houses.
He stopped to eat
in a little Cuban place.
He talked
with Cuban people.
They seemed
like brothers and sisters.
Mario spoke Spanish
wherever he went.

For the first time
in 20 years,
Mario felt really Cuban.
He felt good.

Mario Lopez
checked into a hotel.
It was a big white house.
The door
was painted orange.
There were tall palm trees
out front.
The hotel
was run by Cubans.
No one questioned

Mario's name.
No one looked at him
as strange.
A young Cuban man
showed Mario
to his room.

From there,
Mario went
to find a boat.
Hundreds of boats
had already gone
to Cuba.
Mario put his name
on a list.
He would have to wait
until a boat came back
from Cuba.

Two days later
a boat was ready.
Mario paid the owner.
He told the man
his parents' names.

"We should be back
in a few days,"
said the man.

Mario waited.
Each minute
seemed like an hour.
Each hour
seemed like a day.
He looked
at his watch
a hundred times.

The sun
began to set.
It was the third day.
Mario waited
along the water.
He was almost ready
to go back
to the hotel.
Then he saw
one more boat
coming toward him.
It started

as a white spot
where the sky
meets the water.
It grew bigger.
At last,
Mario could tell
this was his boat.

He saw hundreds
of strange faces.
Most of them
were young men.
Mario waited
as each person
got off the boat.

And then
he saw them.
Mama and Papa Lopez,
20 years late.

Thinking It Over

1. Where do you
   feel most at home?

2. Is there a part of your town
   that a group of people
   have made their own?

3. How can a place change
   over a long time?

CHAPTER **13**

Mama and Papa
needed a few days
to rest.
Mario stayed with them
in Miami.
They all stayed
in the Cuban hotel.
They ate in Cuban places.
They listened
to Cuban music.

On the third day
Mario knew
it was time to go.
He had to get back
to the bank
and his family.
Coming to Miami
helped Mario see
a part of his roots.
But it was not home.

"Mama and Papa,"
he began.
"I want you
to come to Ohio
with me.
You must meet
my wife and children.
You will love them!
You may live with us."

"Why don't you
bring them to Miami?"
asked Papa.
"Everything here
is so Cuban!
They would love it!"

"No,"
said Mario.
"Their home
is in Ohio.
And so is mine.
I live there.
I work there.
My children
were born there.

They go to school there.
I am part of it.
I must go."

"We will come along,"
said Mama.
"We must meet
your family.
But maybe
we will come back
to Miami.
We will see."

Mario and his parents
boarded the plane.
The big bird took off.
Mario looked
out the window.
He looked down
at Miami below.
He remembered
the first time
he left Miami.
Leaving Miami today
felt different.
Back then,

he was going to Ohio.
Today he was going home.

In a few hours
the plane landed
in Cleveland.
Kathy and the girls
were waiting.

Mario watched his foot
touch the ground.
He looked up
at the blue sky.
The sun was shining.
It was the same sun
as the one over Cuba.
But Mario's life
was right here—
not in Cuba,
not in Miami.

Mario helped his parents
get off the plane.
"We are here!"
he said to them.
"Welcome to my home."

Thinking It Over

1. What is home?

2. Have you ever felt a pull to a place?

3. Can a person really make a new home?